Name: _____

Form: _____

AF172846

Working Scientifically

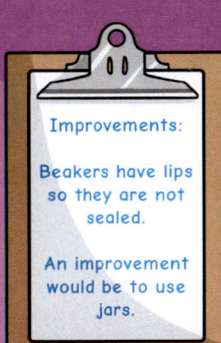

Improvements:

Beakers have lips so they are not sealed.

An improvement would be to use jars.

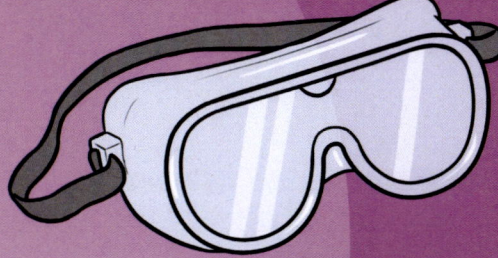

- Read, engage and learn!
- Full colour, illustrated Topic Booklet.
- Glossary of key words, Active Learning Game & Flashcards.
- Ideal for ISEB 13+ Common Entrance and KS3 pupils.

This Oaka™ Books Write Your Own Notes Booklet goes hand in hand with the Active Learning Pack on this topic. The pack includes a Topic Booklet, an Active Learning Game and Question & Answer flashcards.

Fresh Focus on Learning

Working Scientifically Glossary

Accurate: ....
....

Compare: ....
....
....

Conclusion: ....
....
....

Control variables: ....
....
....

Dependent (output) variable:
....
....

Equipment: ....
....

Evaluation: ....
....
....

Experiment: ....
....

Fair Test: ....
....
....

Hypothesis: ....
....

Improvement: ....
....
....

Independent variable: ....
....
....

Line of Best Fit: ....
....
....
....

Measurements: ....
....
....

Method: ....
....
....

Outliers: ....
....

Reliability: ....
....
....

Risk Assessment: ....
....
....

Conducting An Experiment

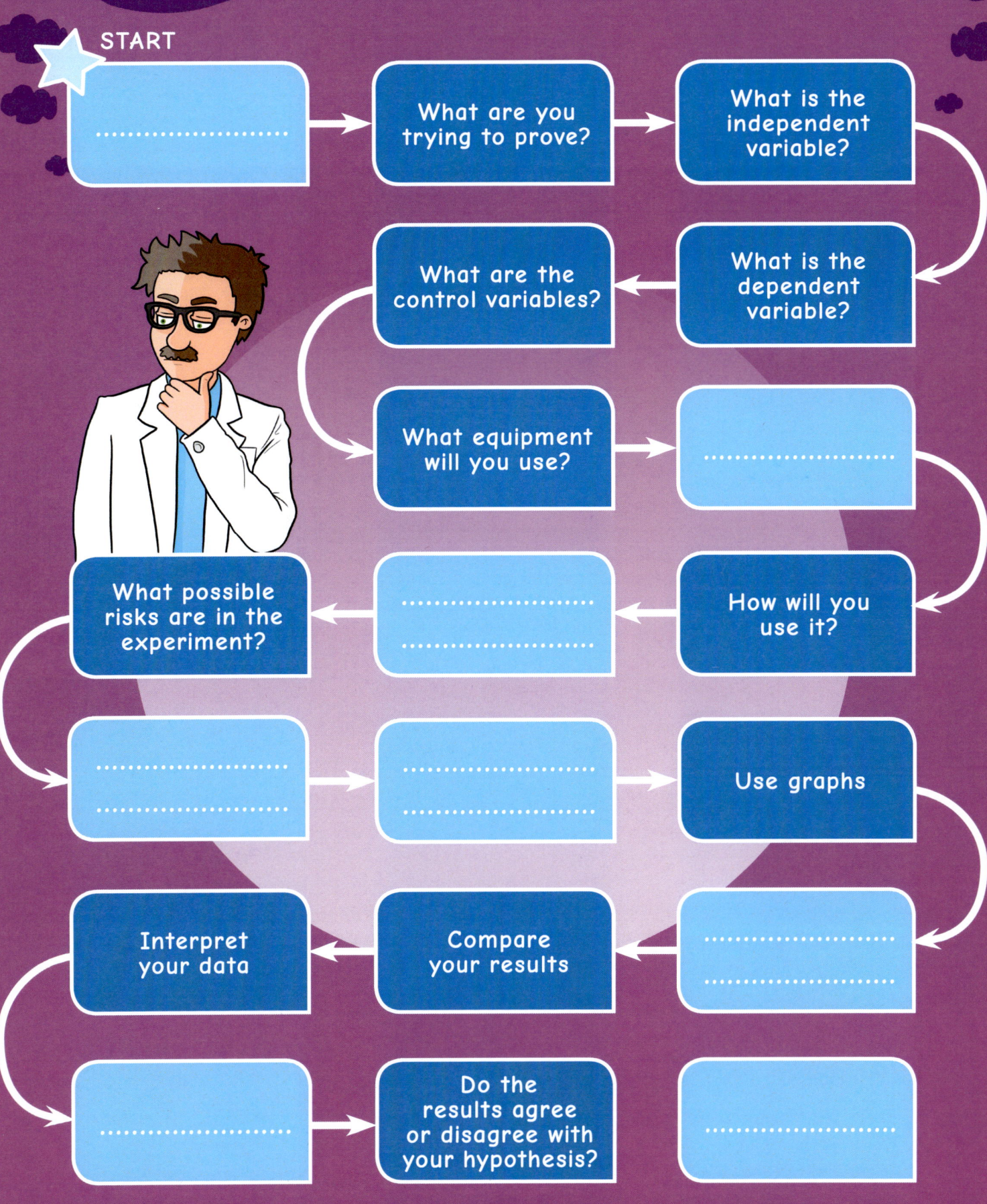

START

....

What are you trying to prove?

What is the independent variable?

What are the control variables?

What is the dependent variable?

What equipment will you use?

....

What possible risks are in the experiment?

....
....

How will you use it?

....

....

Use graphs

Interpret your data

Compare your results

....
....

....

Do the results agree or disagree with your hypothesis?

....

1   Why Does That Happen?

• Scientists try to work out .... things happen.

Why can one person jump higher than another?

Why can one car go faster than another?

Why does one cow produce more milk than another?

2   Guessing

• We can guess a ....

• But it may or may not be true.

• That's because it has not been ....

I guess that....

3   Hypothesis (hipe-oth-ess-sis)

• This means that the .... is just a .... reason.

• Scientists call it a ....

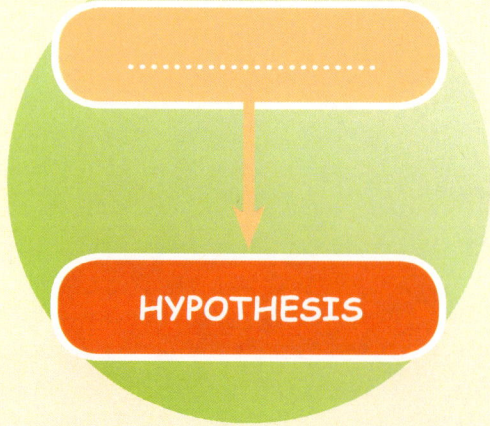

....

HYPOTHESIS

Fill in the blanks using these words to help you...
one   collection   conduct   aim   information
true   hypothesis   experiment   prove

4 Is The Hypothesis True?

- So, how do we work out if a .... is true or not?

- We .... (do) an experiment.

Let's conduct an experiment!

5 What Is An Experiment?

- It is the .... of data (......................................).

- This will tell us if the hypothesis is .... or not.

6 The Aim

- Before you start an experiment, you need to have an .... (the hypothesis).

- What are you trying to ....?

7 My experiment is...

- Make your aim about .... thing.

- Do say: 'My .... is to investigate the effect of sunlight on the growth of a plant.'

8 Don't Make It General

- Do .... say 'I'm going to look at how plants grow.'
- This is too general.
- If you change more than one thing, it will not be a fair test.

Make sure to be ....!

9 Making Experiments Count

Experiments need to be:

....

....

Able to be ....

10 What is a Variable?

- Anything in an experiment that we can .... is called a variable.

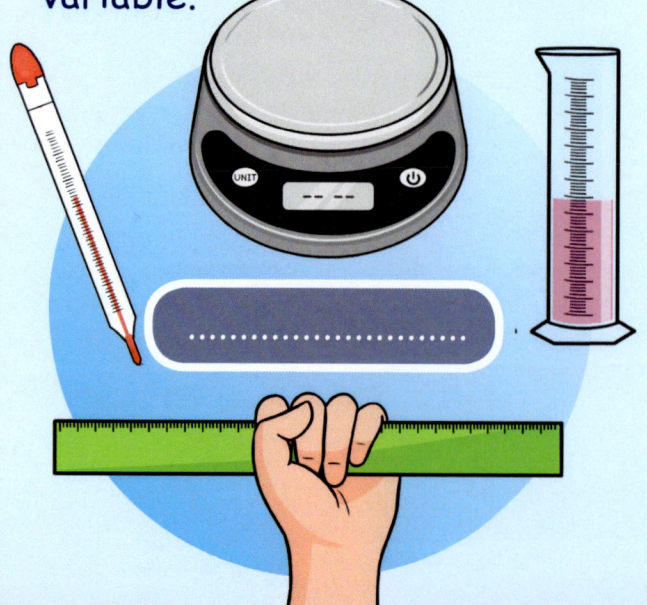

....

11 Things That Change

- There are .... (also known as input) variables.
- These are things than we can ....

What can I change in my ....?

12 Things That Are Affected

- There are .... (or output) variables.

- These are .... by the independent ....

The more sunlight (the input variable) there is...

...the bigger the plant grows (output variable)

13 Choosing .... Thing

- If you were investigating the .... of light on plant growth, the independent .... could be:

"The number of hours of light the plant is given each day."

14 Things That Stay The Same (Control Variables)

- There are things that are .... changed.

- These are the .... variables.

- Things that would stay the .... (control variables) would be:

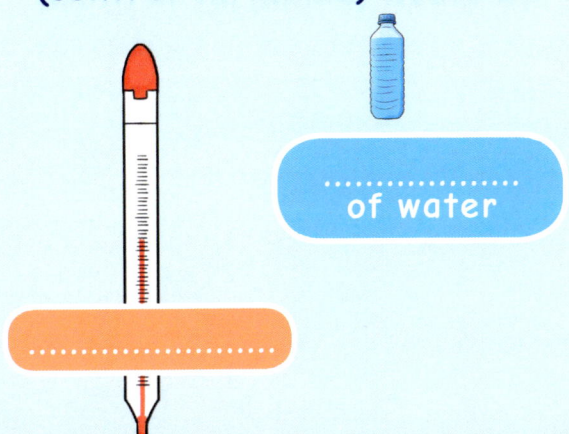

.... of water

amount of soil used

.... of soil used

type of plant used

....

15   The Dependent Variable

- The dependent variable (or .... variable) will be the .... of the ....

- So growth will be .... (changed) by the amount of .... it is given.

dependent variable = growth of the plant

16   A Fair ....

To make your experiment a .... test you need to:

only change one .... at a time!

17   A .... Result = Average Readings

- .... your experiment.

- Take an average reading. Add up your .... and divide then by the number of times you have done the test:

5cm   6cm   7cm

- If your plant grew 5cm on the first test, 7cm on the second and 6cm on the third.

- Add 5cm + 6cm + 7cm = 18cm

- 18cm .... by 3 = 6cm

6cm is the .... growth!

18   Equipment

- Use the right equipment to measure ....
- .... measurements are important.
- Measure on flat ....

WRONG!   CORRECT!

19   Ruler

- Use rulers for measuring ....
- .... from 0 mm.

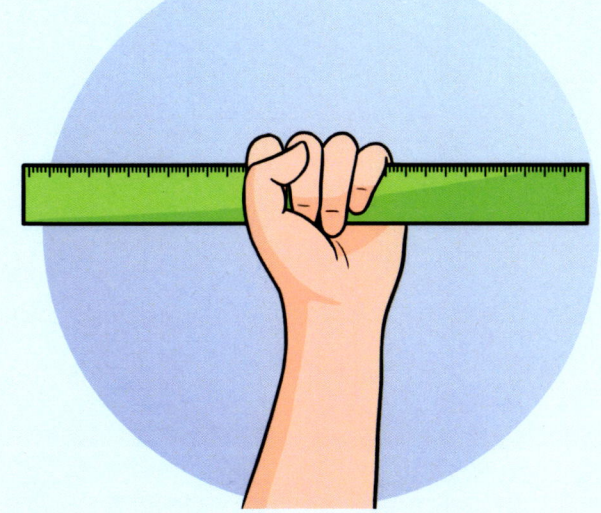

20   Glass or Plastic?

- Use .... beakers for hot liquids.
- Plastic beakers can melt or change shape.

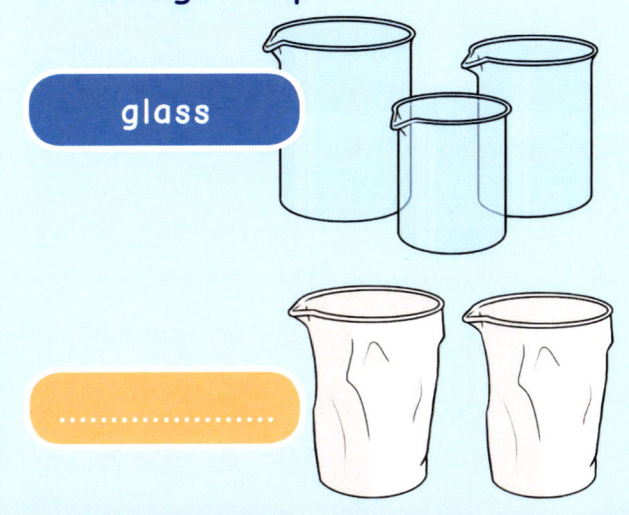

glass

....

21   Measuring Liquids

- Use measuring cylinders for measuring ....
- Measure the .... part of the liquid.

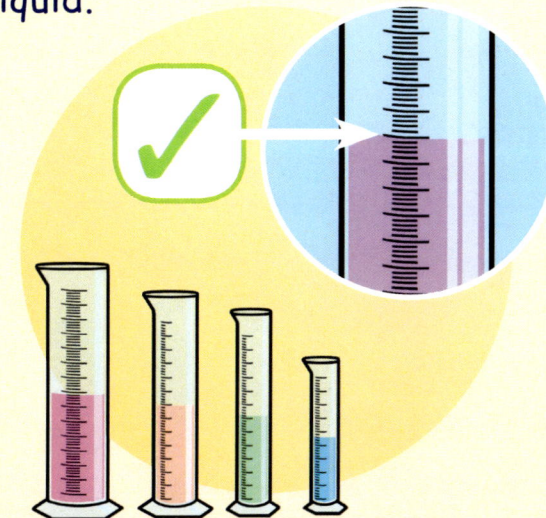

22 .... Liquids

- If you measure ....,
remember:

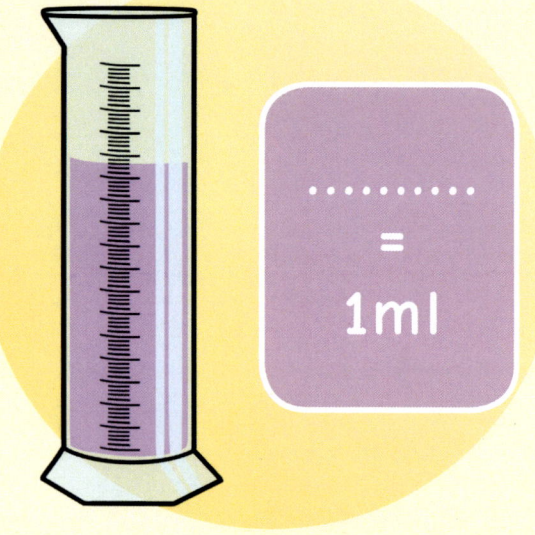

$$\ldots\ldots\ldots\ldots = 1ml$$

23 Weighing Solids

- If you weigh a .... in a dish, you need to:

- Weigh the .... (A).

A

24 Weighing Solids

- .... the dish with the solid (B).

B

25 Weighing Solids

- Take away A from B.

$$B - A = Xg$$

- X is the .... of the solid.
- You are now left with the answer!

26   What Are The ....?

Think about all the .... risks:

• .... from a bunsen ....

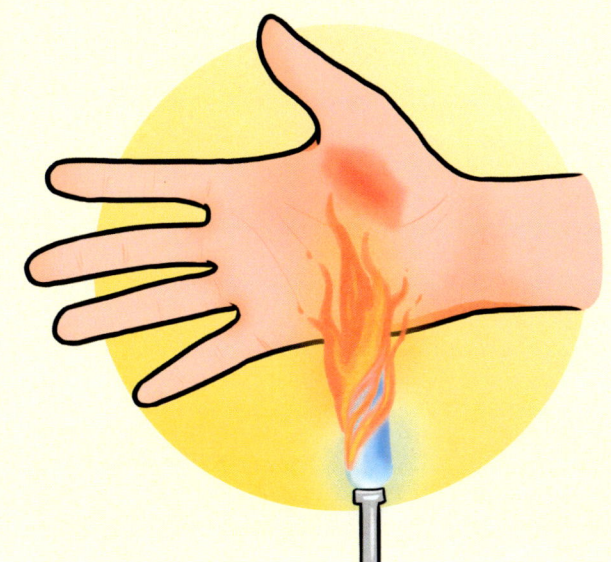

27   Long Hair

• .... long hair.

28   Spilt ....

• Getting chemicals in your ....

29   Glass Breaking

• Danger of a test .... or beaker ....

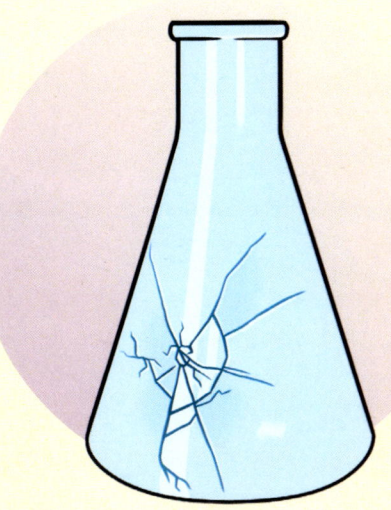

This booklet is not to be photocopied. Thank you.

8

Fill in the blanks using these words to help you...
beakers no apron safety flames
tight clothing long lids

30 Safety ....

- Wear an ....
- Take care with naked ....

31 Working Safely

- Tie back .... hair.
- .... dangling shirt sleeves.

32 Safety Goggles

- Wear .... goggles.
- Keep .... on chemical bottles.

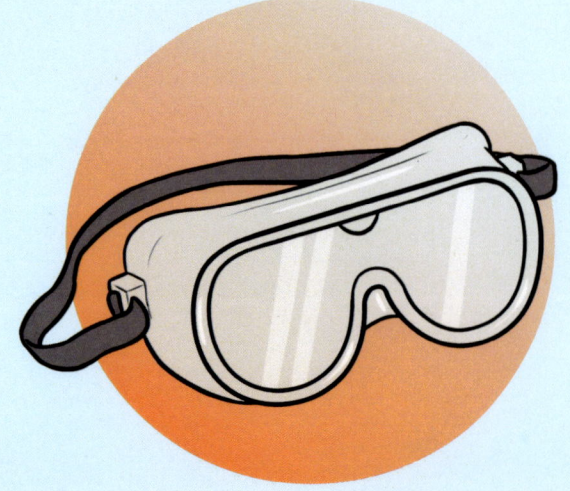

33 Using Equipment

- Don't make clamps too ....
- Put .... on flat surfaces.

34 An ....

- Let's carry out an experiment.
- The .... will be the same for any experiment you do.

Time to experiment!

35 Hypothesis

- First write your ....
- This could be 'I think that the amount of .... will affect how long a candle burns'.

36 Independent ....

- Now we need to see if it is true!
- Identify the independent variable (the bit you will ....).
- This could be the .... of the beaker you put your candles in.

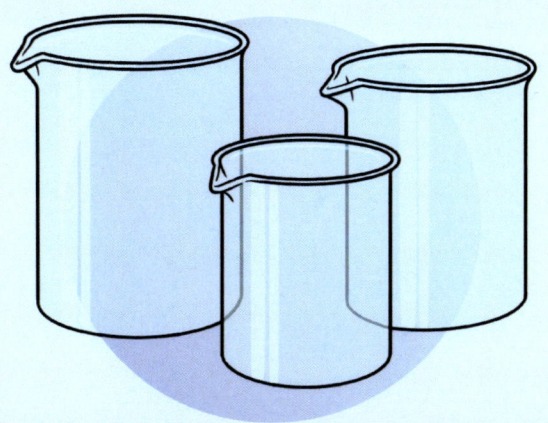

37 .... Variable

- .... the dependent variable (the thing that will be changed by the .... variable).
- This is the time it takes for the .... to go out.

38 **What is the Control Variable?**

- This is using the same .... and size of candle for each ....

39 **Write A ....**

What equipment will you use?

- different sized ....
- tea lights.
- ....
- heat proof mat.

40 **How Will You Use It?**

- Place a tea light on a .... proof mat.
- .... it and place a beaker over it.

41 **Repeat the Experiment**

- Time how .... it takes for the candle to go out.
- .... for each of the beakers.
- Then repeat your experiment.
- Work out an .... of the results.

42 Making It A .... Test

- **Remember**: make sure you only change one .... at a time during the experiment.

- In this experiment, it will be the ....

43 The Results

- Plan your table of results.

- What will you ....?

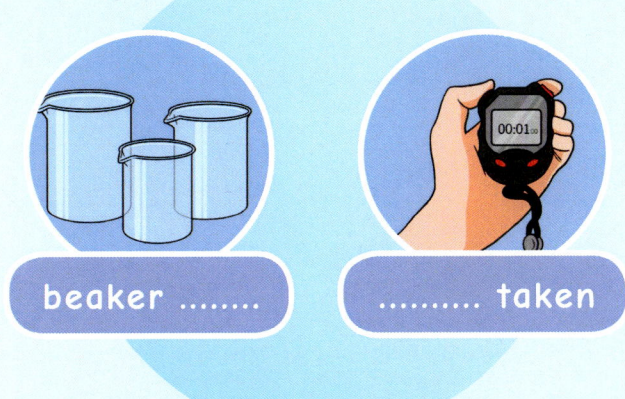

beaker .... taken

44 .... the Risks

Make a table for your .... assessment.

What is the risk?	The	Reducing the risk

45 Do The ....

- Now you can do the experiment and put your .... in the table.

Beaker size	Time taken

46   Drawing a ....

• Use a sharp .... and a ruler.

Remember:
x axis - .... variable.
y axis - dependent variable.

47   Which Graph?

• For this experiment we have numbers for .... variables.

• So, a .... graph is best.

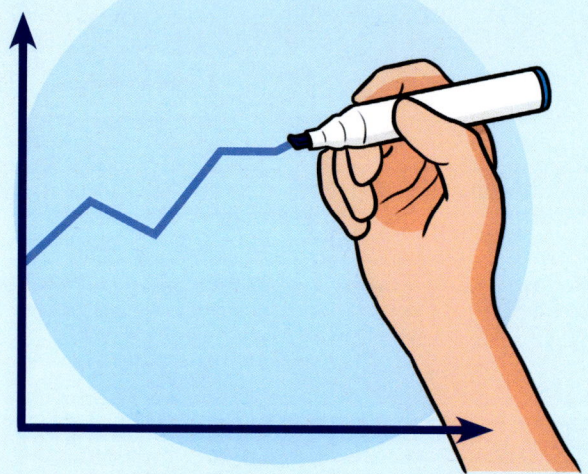

48   Bar Chart

• Remember: if you had only .... variable that was numbers then a .... chart would be best.

49   Line of Best Fit (not required for CE)

• On your line graph draw the line of .... fit.

• Go through as many .... as possible.

• The line can be .... or curved.

line of best fit

50 **Odd Results (not required for CE)**

- The line of best fit will show any .... results.

- These are called ....

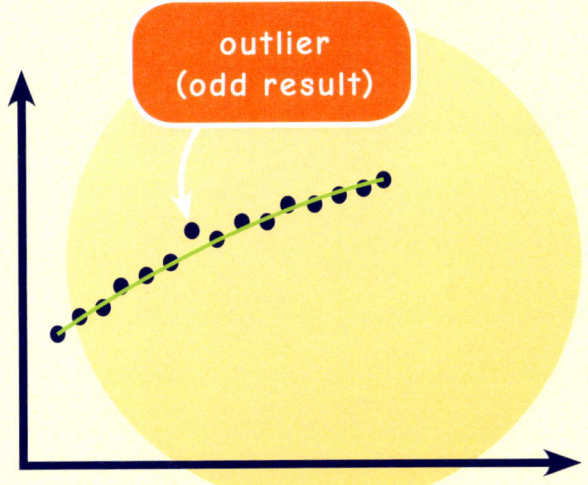

outlier (odd result)

51 .... **The Results**

- Write a sentence to explain the ....

- My results show that the .... lasts longest in the .... beaker.

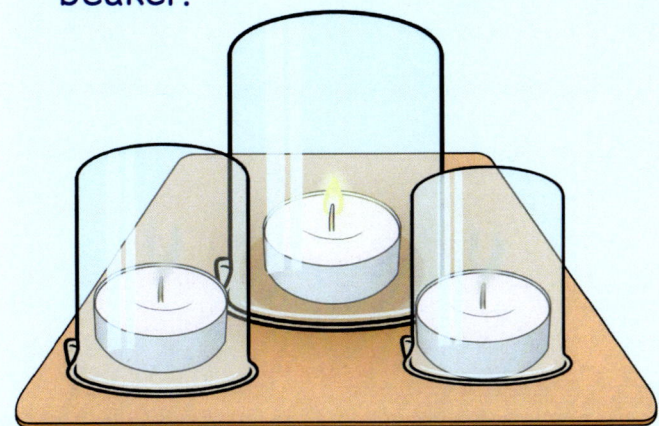

52 .... **The Results**

- How long did the flame last in each of the ....? Give details.

In the 500ml beaker, the flame lasted x seconds.

In the 300ml beaker, the flame lasted y seconds.

Whereas in the 150ml beaker, it only lasted z seconds.

53 Now .... **What You Saw (Conclusion)**

- Why do you think this happened?

The flame lasted .... in the biggest beaker because there was more ....

- This is OK and will get you some marks BUT....

54 Go For More Marks!

- A better .... might be:

> The 500ml beaker had the largest volume of ....
>
> This meant that the candle could burn for longer as oxygen is needed for ....
>
> As the candle burned, CO_2 was produced and O_2 was used up.
>
> This took longer in the biggest .... because there was more oxygen to start with.

55 How could you .... the experiment?

Think about how you could make your experiment .... and why!

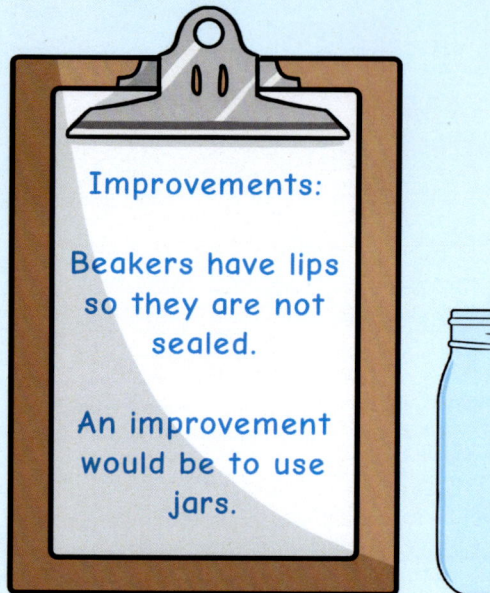

Improvements:

Beakers have lips so they are not sealed.

An improvement would be to use jars.

56 How did you make it a .... test?

- The experiment was done 3 times for each of the .... variables (the size of the beaker).

- This made the .... more reliable.

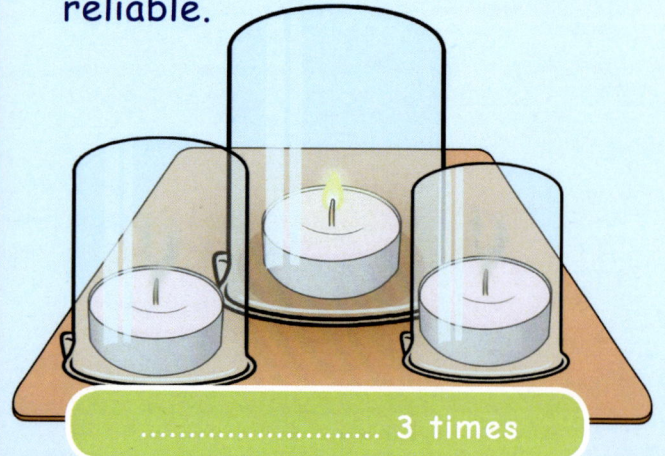

.... 3 times

57 How did you make it a fair test?

- Just one .... was changed.

Conducting An ....

.... (What are you trying to prove?):

.... Variables (What will you change?):

.... Variables (What is going to change?):

.... Variables (What will you keep the same?):

.... (What will you use?):

.... (How will you do the experiment?):

.... (What happened?):

.... (How did the results compare with the different independent variables?):

.... (What could you do to make the experiment more reliable?):

About Oaka Books

Fresh Focus on Learning

Children learn best when they are engaged...

Our aim is to help children enjoy learning by making it fun! That way they will succeed.

This Topic Pack is based on the ISEB 13+ Common Entrance and National Curriculum guidelines for KS3.

The design and layout of our books follow guidelines from the British Dyslexia Association.

Three Easy Steps

Read: the easy to follow bullet point Topic Booklet.

Engage: Play the Active Learning Game.

Learn: When you understand the topic, test yourself using the Write Your Own Notes Book. You can use the Topic Booklet to help if you get stuck.

One (short) Topic at a time:

For some students, a big book is a big turn off. That's why we focus on one topic at a time. Short and to the point.

Reading Age

This booklet is suitable for children with a reading age of 10 years.

Topic Packs for KS1, KS2 & KS3 Include:

History
Geography
Chemistry
Biology
Physics
Maths
French

Please visit www.oakabooks.co.uk for more information about forthcoming titles

First paperback edition printed 2015 in the United Kingdom.
A catalogue record for this book is available from the British Library.

ISBN 978-1-911189-15-2
No part of this book shall be reproduced or transmitted in any form or by any means, electronic or mechanical, including photocopying, recording or by any information retrieval system without written permission of the copyright owner or a licence permitting restricted copying issued by the Copyright Licensing Agency Ltd, Saffron House, 6-10 Kirby Street, London EC1N 8TS Tel: 020 7400 3100   Fax: 020 7400 3101   Email: cla@cla.co.uk   Web: www.cla.co.uk

Designed, set and published by Oaka™ Books.

To order other titles from Oaka™ Books, please email info@oakabooks.co.uk or visit www.oakabooks.co.uk, or phone: +44 (0) 2392 388519.

Acknowledgements
Our huge thanks go to the many teachers who have been involved in the development of this series of learning guides. Special thanks to Joy Gardiner, for producing hundreds of illustrations, to Kate Doehren, for her enthusiasm and invaluable assistance to my wonderful daughter Sophie, for being the inspiration for the books and, of course, to Charlie, for believing in them.

ISBN 978-1-911189-95-4
CE/KS3/KS4
Working Scientifi-
Write Your Own Notes Booklet

ISBN 978-1-911189-15-2   Produced in association with Kate Doehren, MA Ed, B.Ed Hons, RSA Dip, Sp LD/Dyslexia
Head of Learning Support, Hurstpierpoint College
© Copyright Oaka™ Books 2018